W9-CQZ-759

Donald Crews
Parade

A MULBERRY PAPERBACK BOOK • New York

For all of you

I always remember

and for any of you

I sometimes forget

Manufactured in China.
13 SCP 15 14 13 12

Library of Congress Cataloging in Publication Data
Crews, Donald. Parade.
Summary: Illustrations and brief text present the various elements of a parade—the spectators, street vendors, marchers, bands, floats, and the cleanup afterwards.
1. Parades—Juvenile literature.
[1. Parades—Pictorial works] I. Title.
GT3980.C73 1983 394´.5 82-20927
ISBN 0-688-06520-1

First Mulberry Edition, 1986

NO
PARADE
TODAY
PARKING

Buttons, balloons, and flags for sale. Hot dogs, pretzels, ice cream, and soda to buy.

ICE CREAM

CANDY

SODA

Watchers gather.

A crowd.   Waiting.

Here it
comes!

Flags flying.

A strutting
drum major
leads the
marching band.

cornets, trumpets, flutes,

French horns   **sousaphones,**

field drums, cymbals, and last the big bass drums.

Here comes a float,

and baton twirlers, twirling and turning.

Bicycles from
bygone days,

and antique
automobiles,

a cruise ship,

SAILING/SAILING

and at the end
of the parade,
the brand-new
fire engine.

Nothing left
to see,
nothing left
to do except . . .

clean up.